BATMAN™

ULTIMATE PAINT BOX
BOOK TO COLOR

BATMAN created by Bob Kane

Copyright © 2014 DC Comics.
BATMAN and all related characters
and elements are trademarks of and © DC Comics.
(s14)

BEND33624

bendon®

The BENDON name, logo, and Tear and Share are
trademarks of Bendon, Ashland, OH 44805.

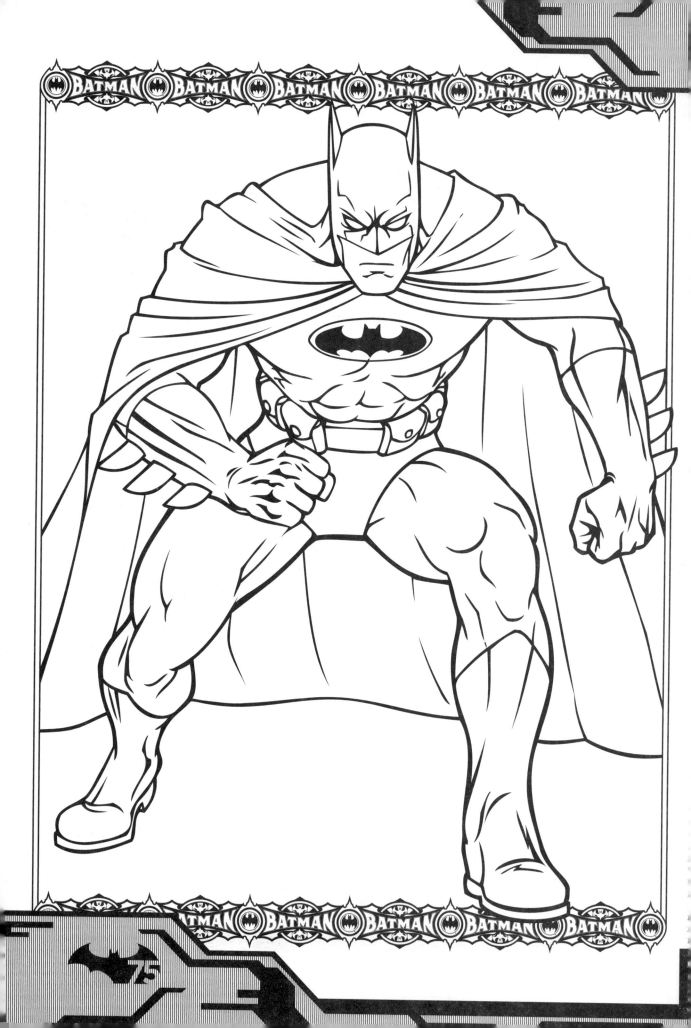

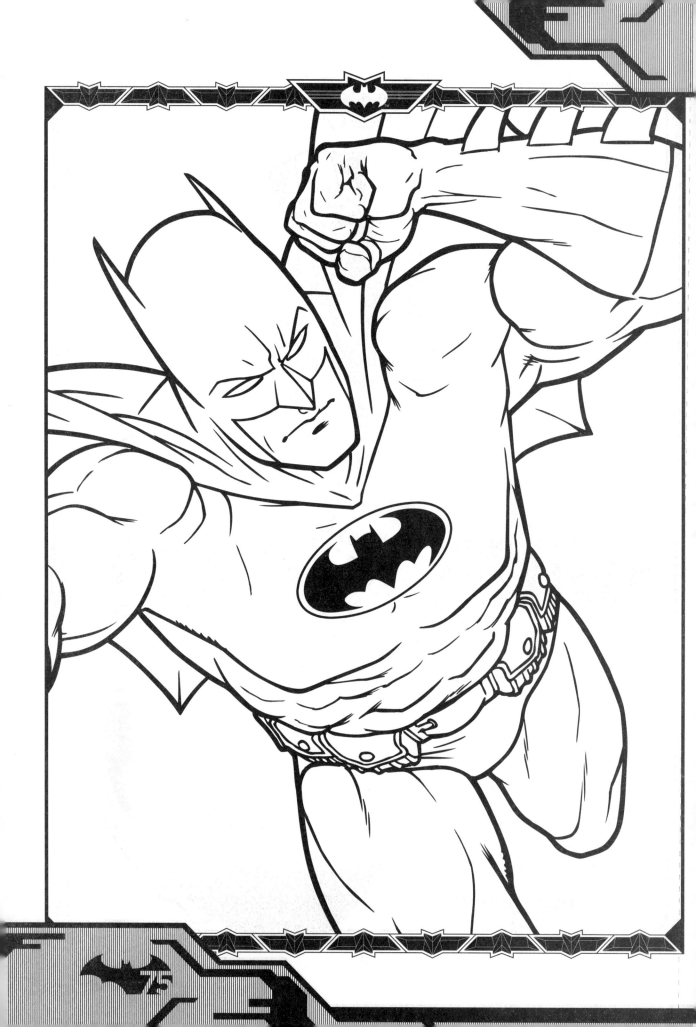

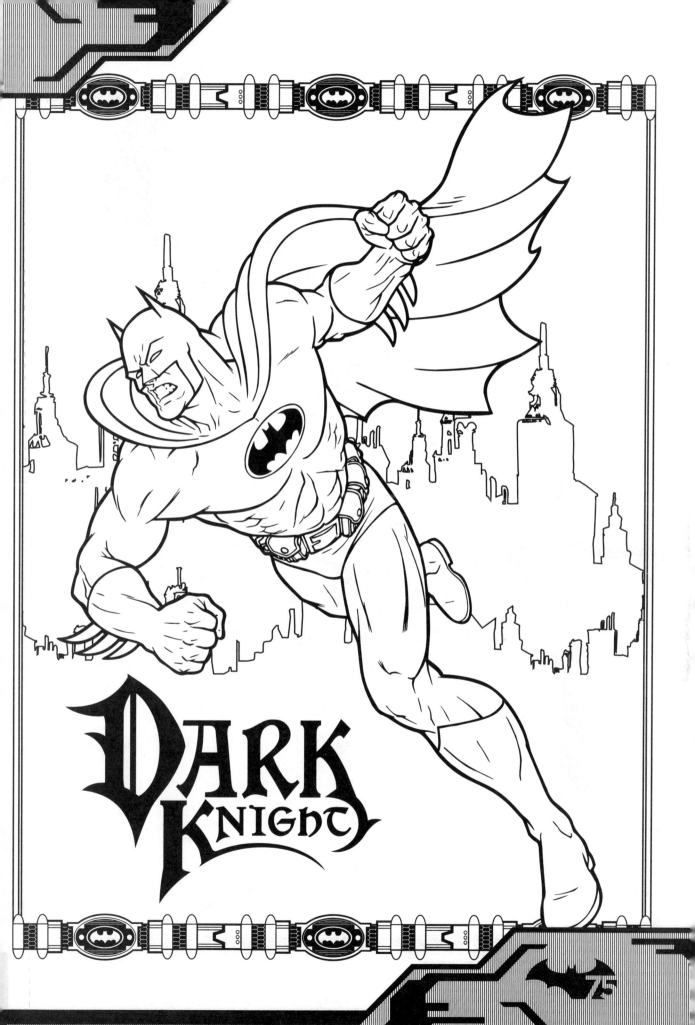

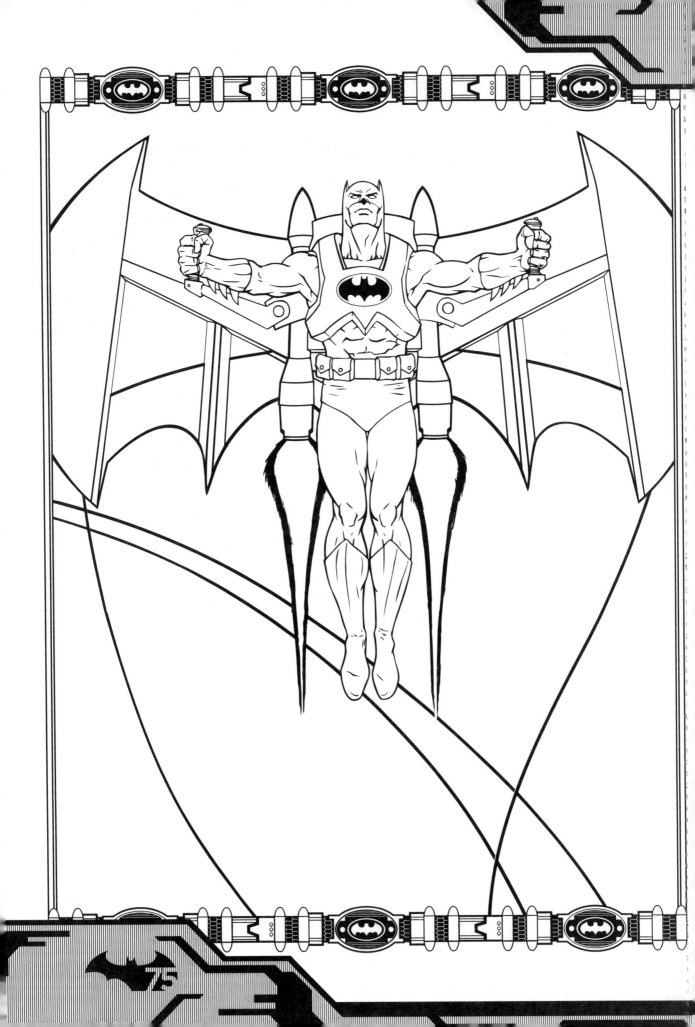

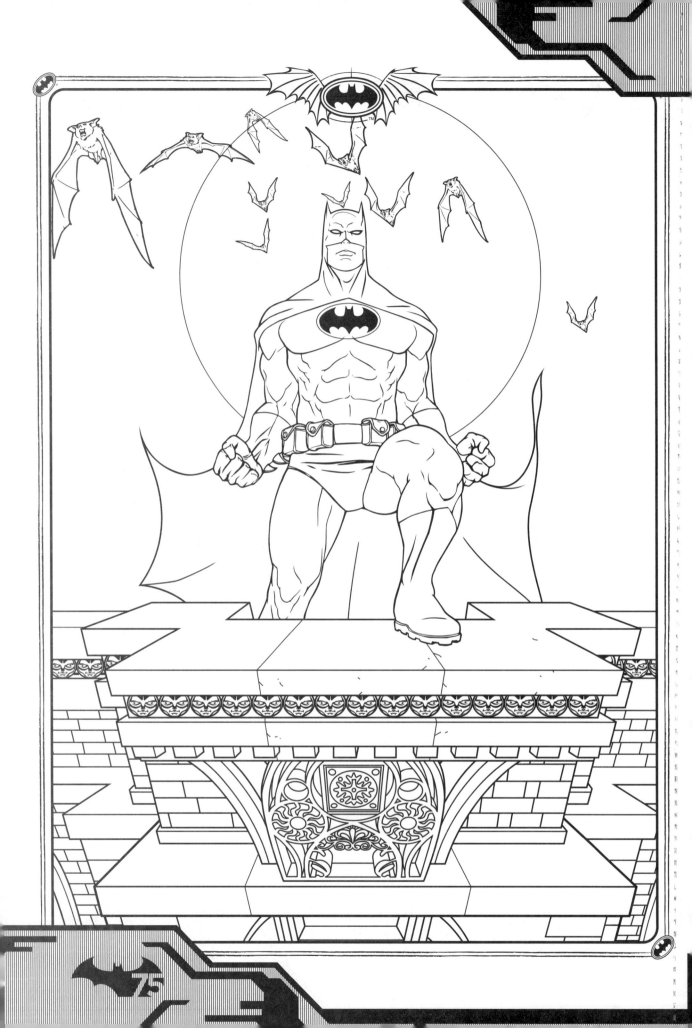

BATMAN

VS

THE PENGUIN

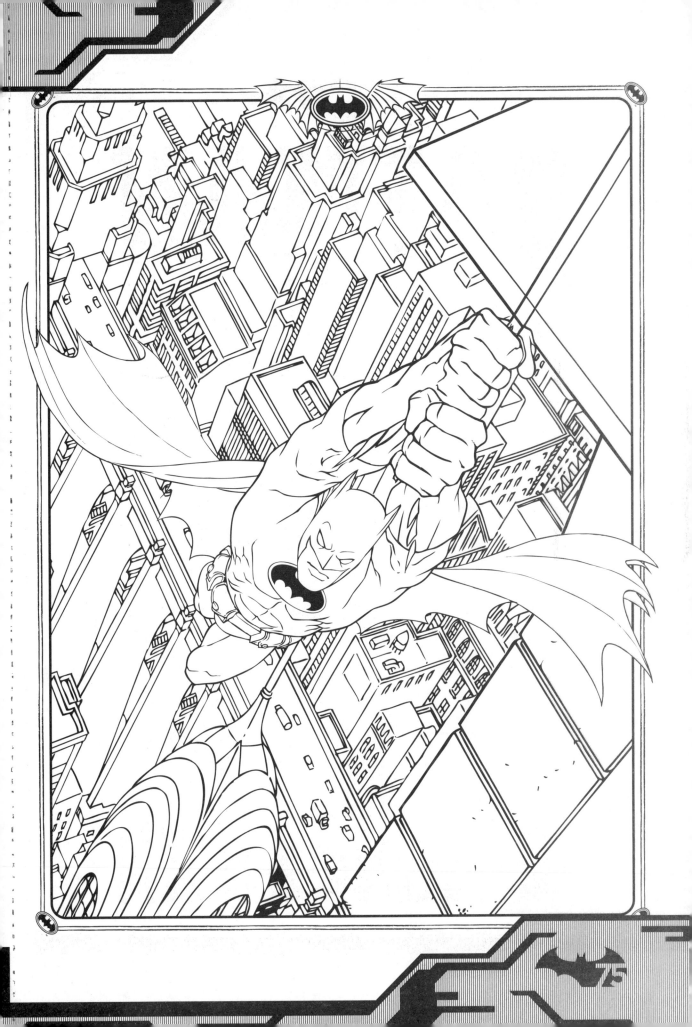

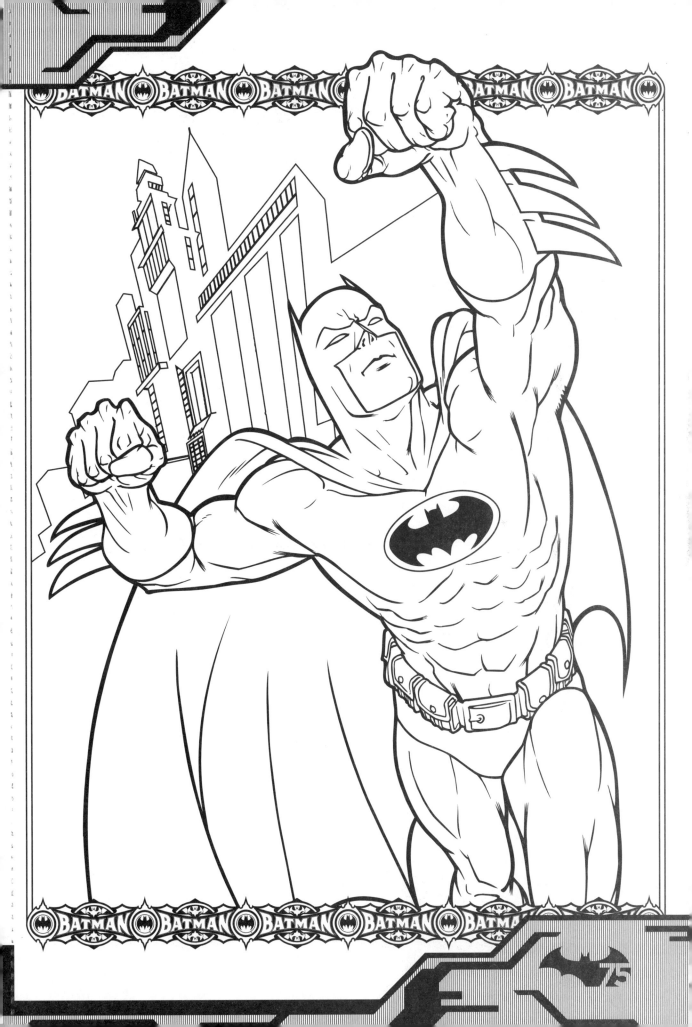

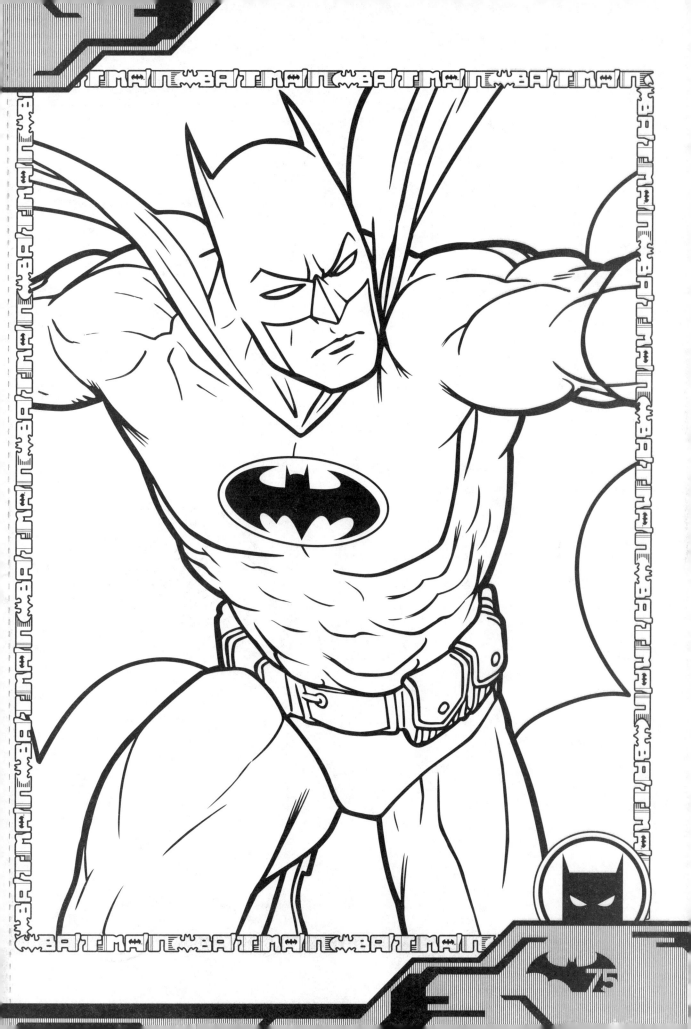

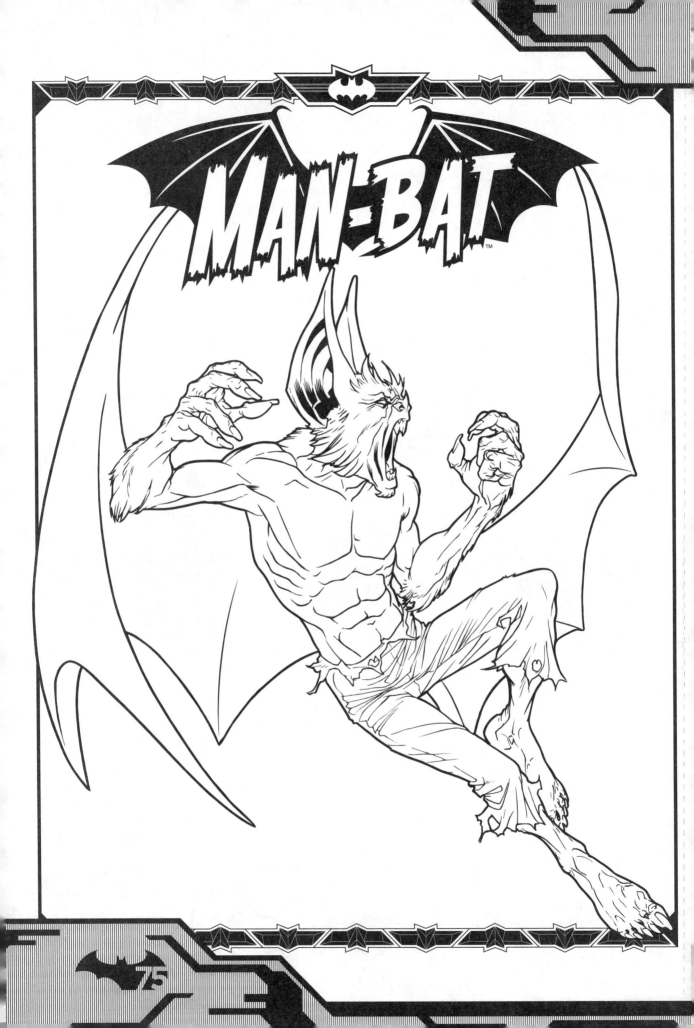

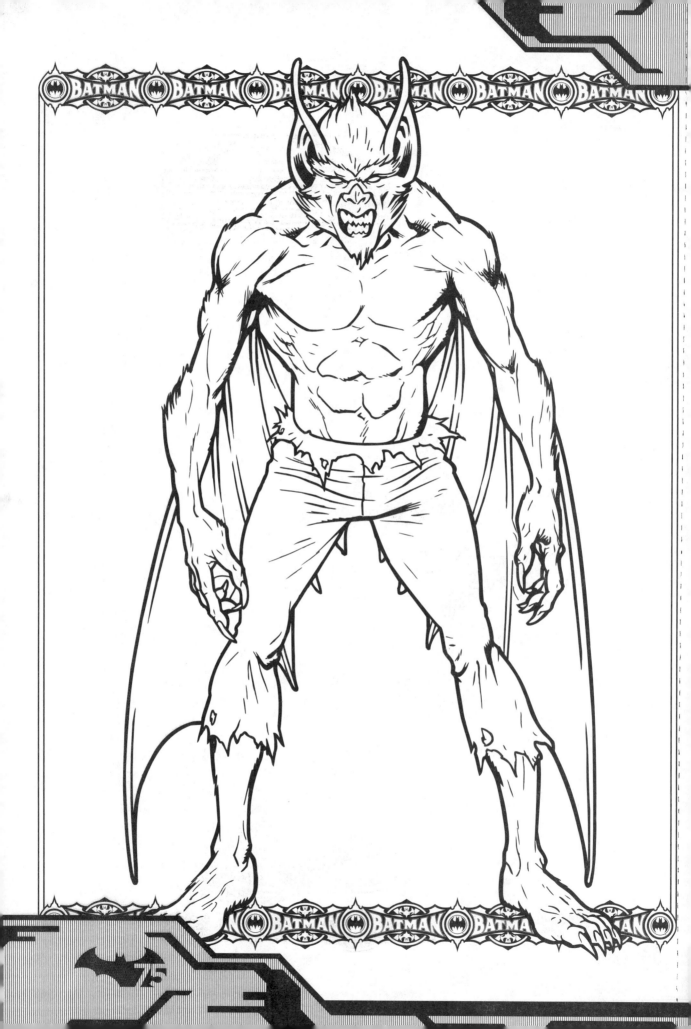

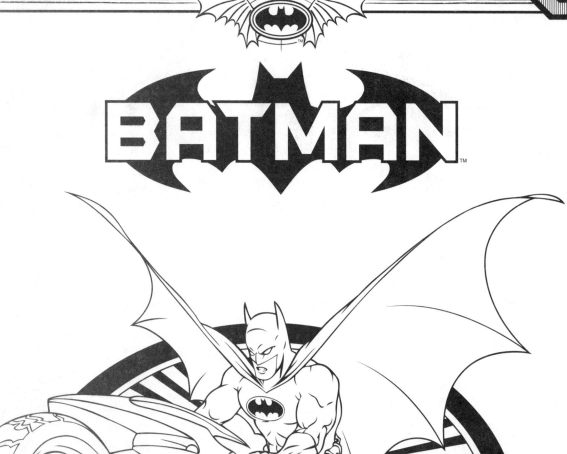